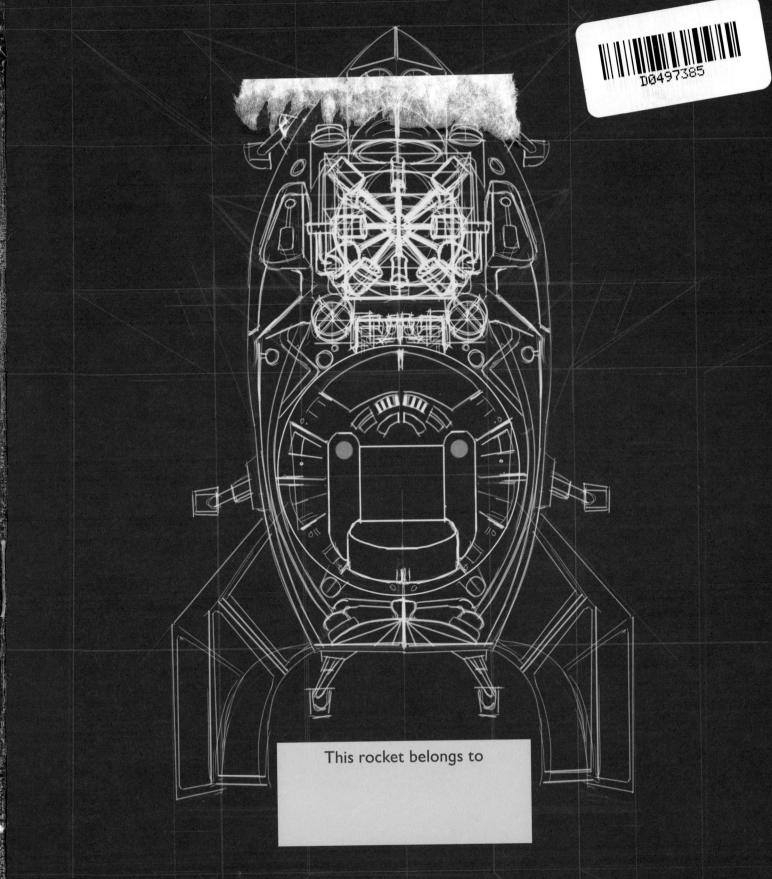

This rocket belongs to

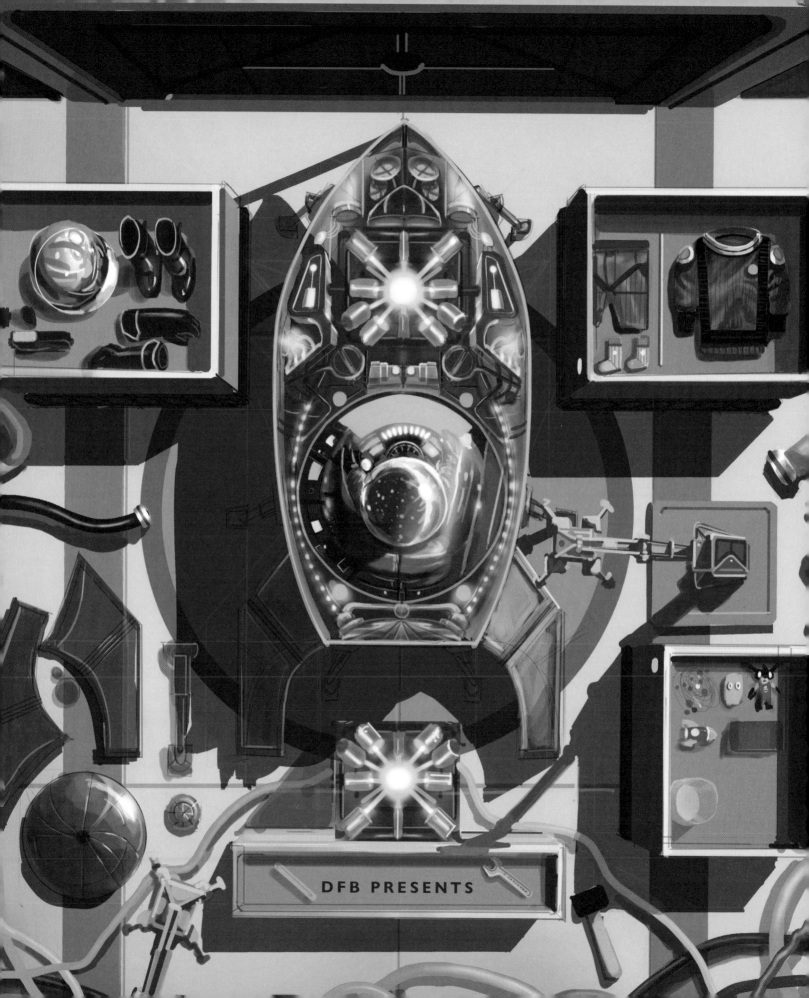

TINY LITTLE ROCKET is a DAVID FICKLING BOOK
First published in Great Britain in 2018 by David Fickling Books,
31 Beaumont Street, Oxford, OX1 2NP
This edition published in 2020
978-1-910989-71-5
www.davidficklingbooks.com
Text © David Fickling, 2018
Illustrations © Richard Collingridge, 2018
1 3 5 7 9 10 8 6 4 2

WARNING : This book will make you want to B L A S T O F F into outer space!
Papers used by David Fickling Books are from well-managed forests
and other responsible sources.

DAVID FICKLING BOOKS Reg. No. 8340307

A C I P catalogue record for this book is available from the British Library.
Design et al design consultants. Printed and bound in China by Toppan Leefung

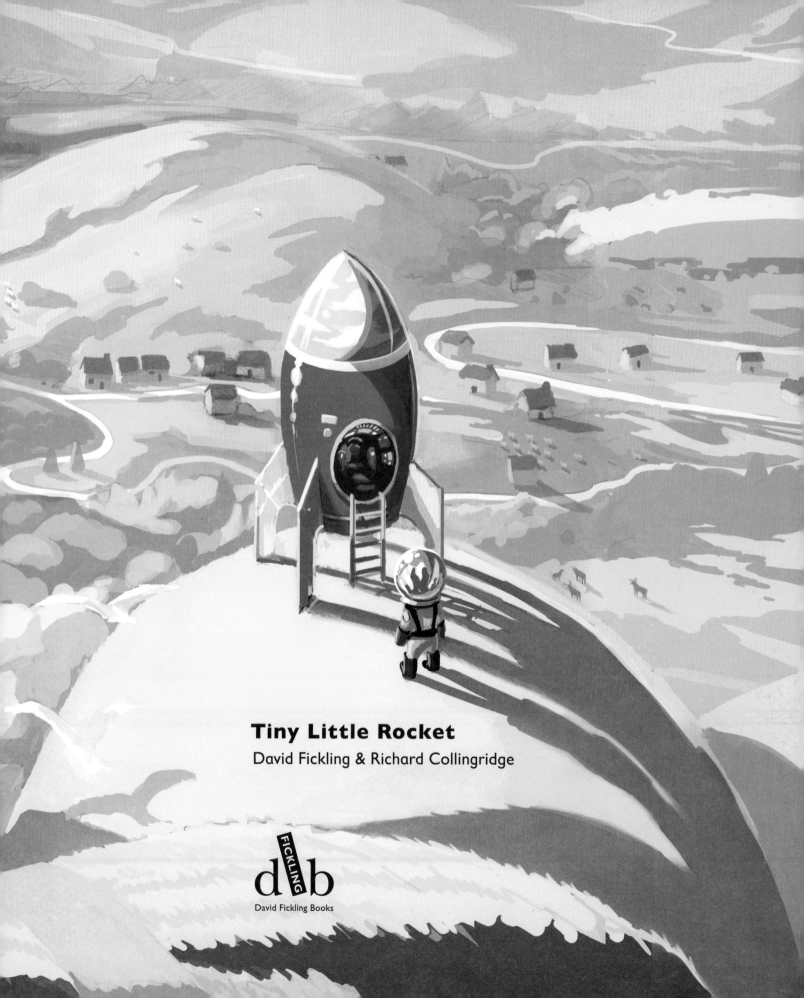

Tiny Little Rocket

David Fickling & Richard Collingridge

David Fickling Books

There's a tiny little rocket
that will take you to the stars.

It only flies there once a year,
but zips you out past Mars.

Its fins are solid silver
with a door made out of gold.

There's a cosy pilot seat inside
for a person, young or old.

It whizzes out to deepest space
while you hold on by the handle.

And there you'll find the golden sun,
our ever burning candle.

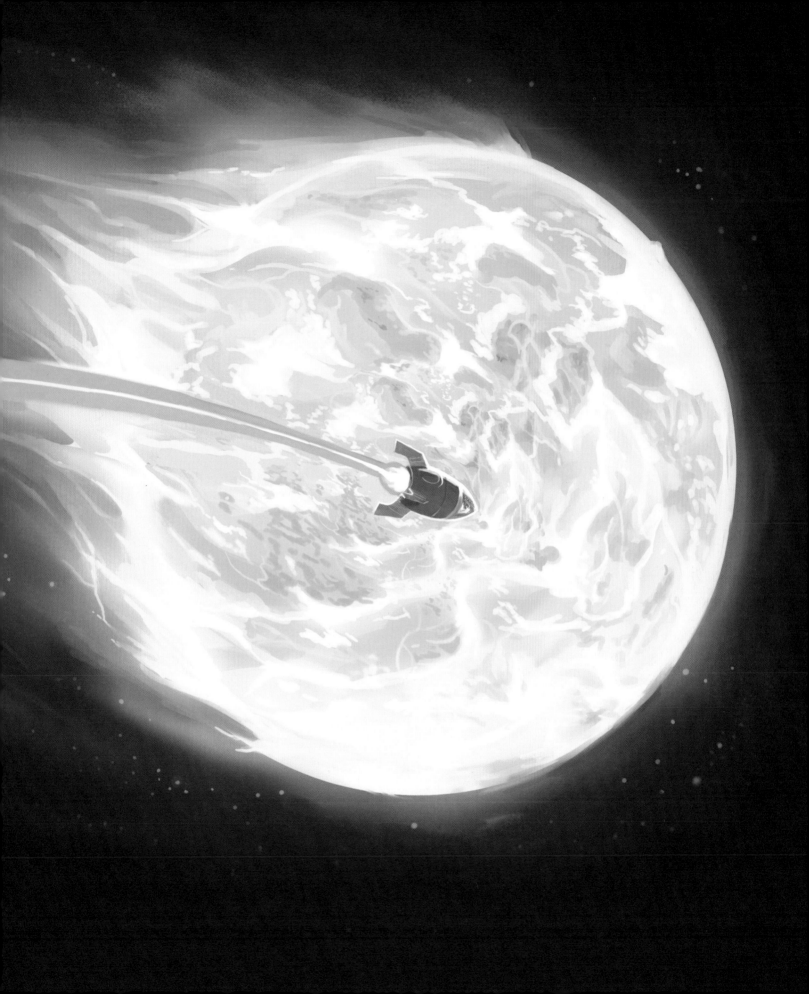

You hang there for a moment
while the rocket hums and clicks.

The sunlight gleams on silver wings;
behind you something ticks.

You see a purple lever
that blares out
PULL ME NOW!

The booster rockets all go
WHOOSH!

You quietly whisper,
WOW!

The little rocket zooms again,

A **HUGE** rock fills the screen.
A **METEOR!**
It's going to **HIT!**

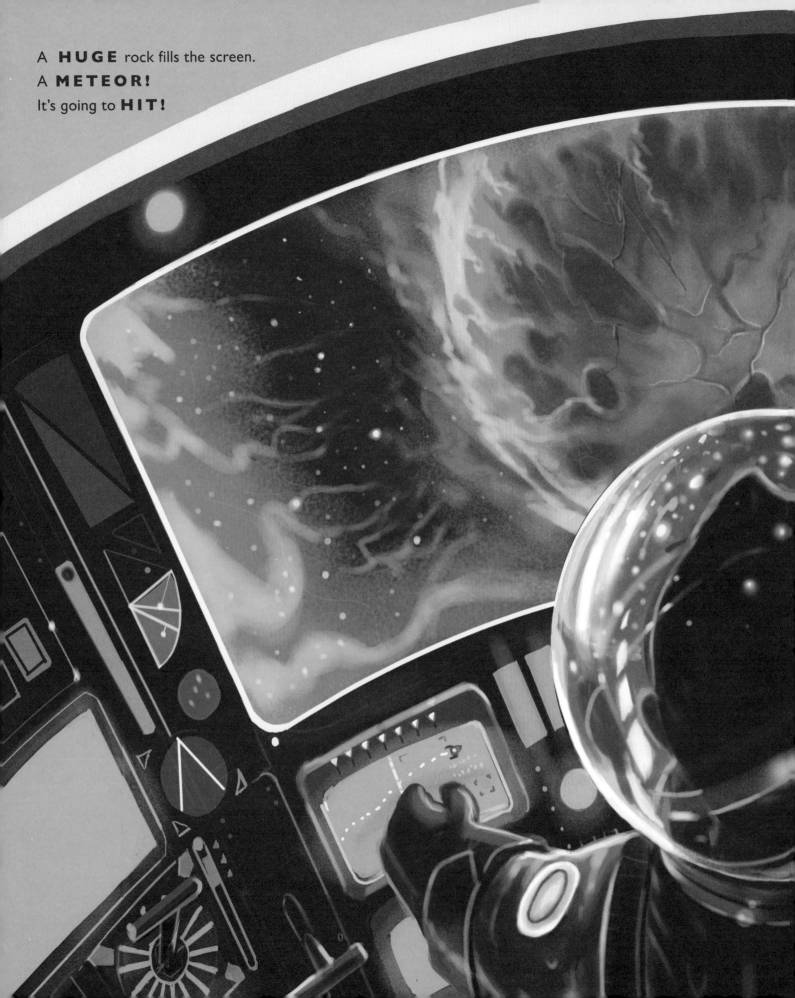

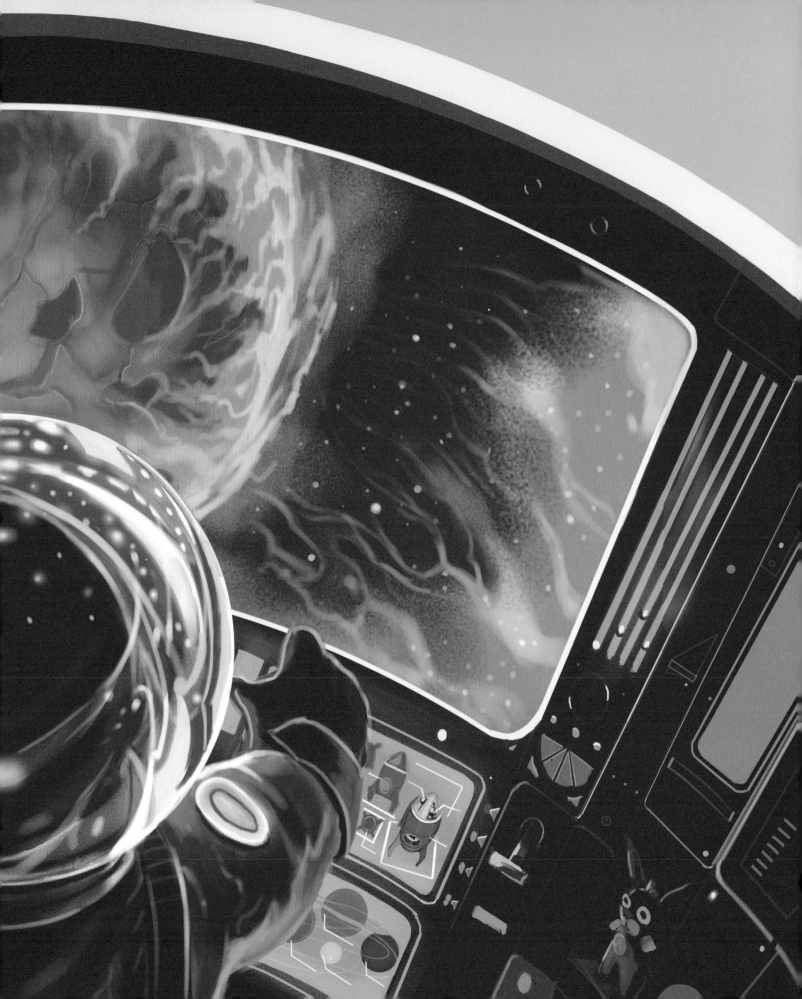

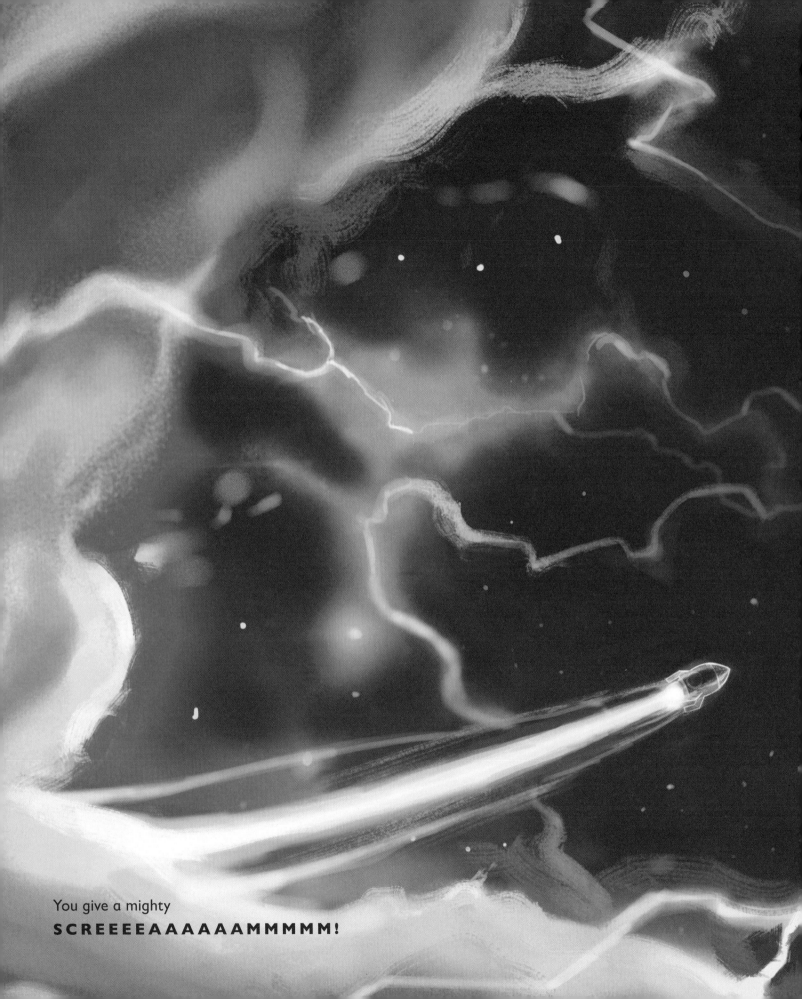

You give a mighty
SCREEEEAAAAAAMMMMM!

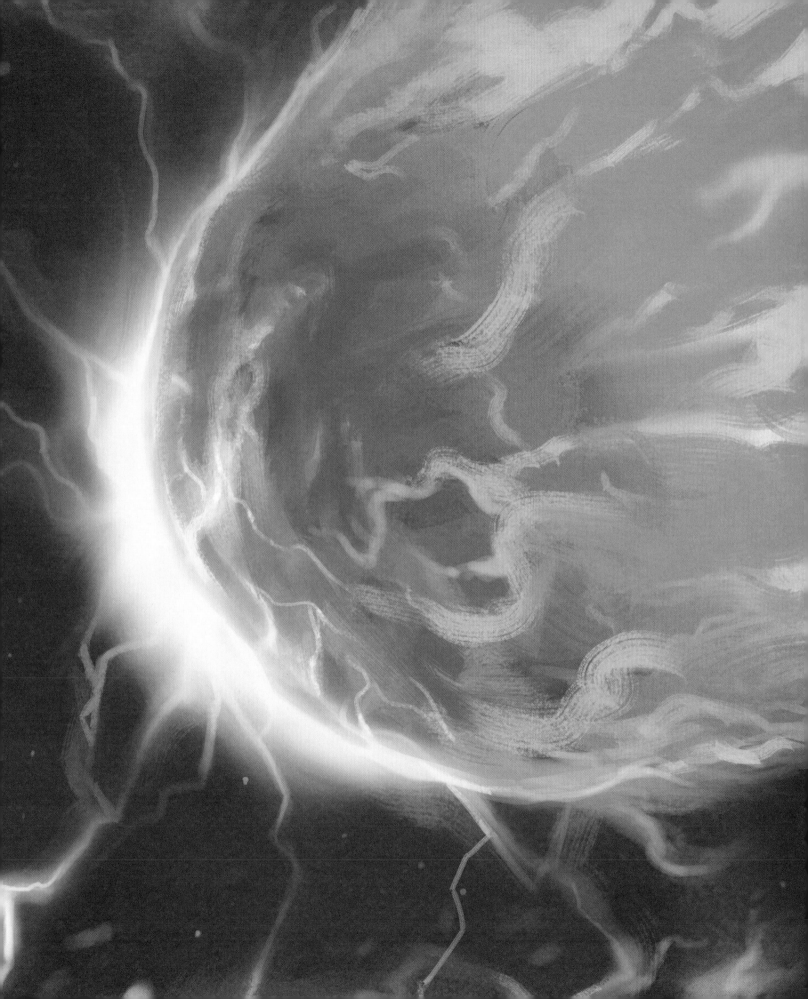

It bops the rocket in the face
and knocks you into outer space!

Round and round the stars do roll,

QUICK!
You'd better take control . . .

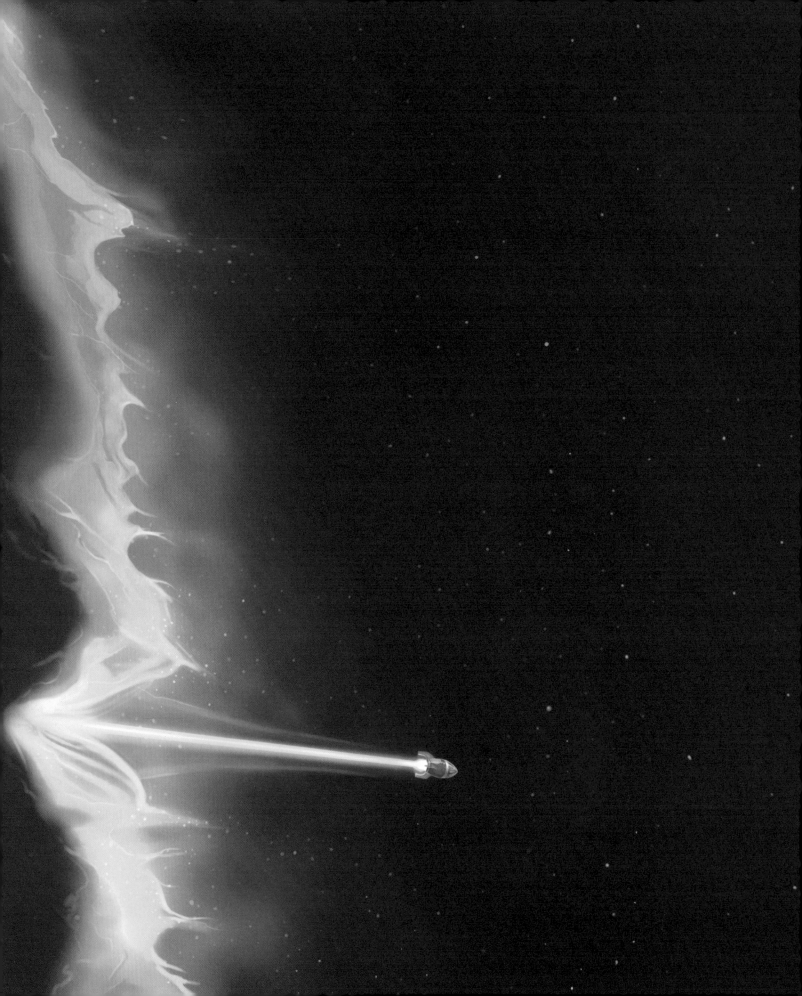

You turn the wheel,
you steer the ship,
your eyes go wide to see.

And like a gorgeous fish of steel
in space you're swimming free!

You dive back through our system,
each planet one by one.

The tiny rocket **ZOOMS** you home
to the third one from the sun.

There's a button on the rocket
that winks just by your head,

and you have to press that
button when it turns from . . .

GREEN to **RED**!

You press the button with
your hand and . . .

. . . a banner is unfurled.
It stretches from the moon to Mars,
saying . . .

Pluto
(Dwarf planet and part of the Kuiper belt)

Neptune

Uranus

Saturn

Earth

HAPPY BIRTHDAY WORLD!

Mars

Jupiter

Mercury

Venus

the sun

Happy Birthday, Earth! (But just how old are you?)

Everybody's birthday is measured in the same way:
by how many times the Earth has gone round the
sun. If you are four years old, then you have been
round the sun four times already, if you are ten then
you have been round ten times.

In a way, the most important birthday of all is the
Earth's own birthday. Nobody knows exactly when the
Earth's first birthday was! However, most scientists
nowadays agree that the Earth is approximately
4.5 billion years old. (That makes roughly 4,500,000,000
times that our amazing planet has circled our
astonishing sun). Millions of people all round the
planet celebrate New Year's Day (the Earth's official
birthday). So, if you were to make a birthday cake
for the Earth it would have roughly 4,500,000,000
candles. But perhaps you don't need to. In the old
days, light was measured in candle power. The sun,
'our ever burning candle' puts out the equivalent of
6,840,000,000,000,000,000,000,000,000 (or
6.84 octillion) candles!! No need for a birthday cake
for the Earth while the sun shines every day.

David Fickling (63 times round the sun)
Richard Collingridge (32 times round the sun)